Timothé

visits the Louvre

Emmanuelle Massonaud
Mélanie Combes

Gründ

Today, Lily is visiting the Louvre museum with
her dad and her friends, Timoté and Maxou.
They arrive in front of its famed glass pyramid.
"Look, kids! there's a man cleaning the diamond-
shaped windows. All six hundred of them!
What a job!"

"But there are also three other pyramids!"
Timoté notices.
"Let's hold hands and go inside," says Lily's dad.

"What a big staircase!" Lily says, impressed.

"Look up!" Lily's dad says, "and admire the Greek statue. It's The Winged Victory of Samothrace."

"But she's lost her head!" Maxou sees.

"Plus her arms are gone!"

"Unfortunately, her arms and head were broken off and never found!"

"But with her wings, it's as if she is flying towards us!" Timoté cries out.

"Look at those cats!" Lily exclaims.
"For Egyptians, cats were sacred.
They symbolized the goddess daughter
of the Sun God!" Lily's dad explains.
"Then long live me! I'm a God!" Maxou cries out.
"I hope not," teases Timoté "or you'll end up
in a sarcophagus... just like them!"

Egyptian antiquities

"Awesome!" says Maxou, fascinated.

"A fighting knight!"

"True!" Timoté notices. "Only his spear is broken!"

"Plus the dragon looks really fierce! Who's going to win, dad?"

"In the end," Lily's dad explains, "the dragon is defeated by Saint George, a brave knight."

Saint Georges
and the dragon
Raphael

"Leonardo da Vinci," Lily's dad explains, "was a great artist who painted this beautiful woman."

"Is that the Mona Lisa?" asks Timoté "Grandpa told me: how lucky you are to visit the Louvre and see the Mona Lisa smile!"

"Hey! Stop pushing me!" Maxou is annoyed. "I can't see a thing!"

The Mona Lisa
Leonardo Da Vinci

"Can anyone recognize the four seasons in these paintings?" asks Lily's dad.

"The flowers are for Spring!" says Lily.

"And that one has cherries!" replies Timoté. "Which means Summer!"

"Bravo! And the one with a crooked nose where nothing grows?"

"Winter!"

"Bravo again! The last painting stands for Autumn."

Summer
Arcimboldo

Spring
Arcimboldo

Winter
Arcimboldo

Autumn
Arcimboldo

"Hey! They're playing our favorite card game. Looks like it's Snap!" says Maxou.
"They may be playing Snap, but that one is cheating!" Timoté answers.
"Why do you say that Timoté?" Lily asks.
"Look carefully!" says Maxou. "Can't you see where he's hiding his cards?"

The Cheat with the Ace
of Clubs
Georges de La Tour

"Is that a princess?" Timoté asks.

"Yes. It's the Infanta Maria Theresa, the King of Spain's daughter."

"She's got a weird haircut!" says Maxou.

"I like the bows in her hair." Lily replies, dreamily.

"The Infanta Maria Theresa married a famous French King. Let's find his portrait."

The Infanta Maria Theresa
Velásquez's Workshop

"Does anyone know the name of this great king?" asks Lily's dad.

"That's Napoleon!" Maxou cries out confidently.

"Wrong!" Timoté knew. "That's the Sun King."

"Exactly!" Says Lily's dad "This is Louis 14th, the Sun King. Napoleon was an emperor, Maxou, not a king."

At the museum bookstore, everyone has chosen a souvenir.

"I chose the painting with the cherries!" says Timoté. "It reminds me of Grandma's marmalade."

"And I, the knight!" Maxou yells out. "Beware you nasty dragon! Here I come!"

While Lily chose 'Spring', which made sense to Timoté, as she was named after a flower.

That night, tired but happy, Timoté decides
to draw a self-portrait. Perhaps one day,
he too will become a great painter like Da Vinci,
Velasquez, La Tour and all of the others!

The End

Let's play and learn with TIMOTÉ!

The Four Seasons

Help Timoté match each season
with Arcimboldo's four paintings.

spring   summer   autumn   winter